PENNY'S PURPOSE

Taylor Morton

Illustrations By
Elle-Allen

To my son Beckett,
you are loved beyond comprehension.

The year was 2015.
I was fluffy, perky, and I had Grinch-feet.

I was running the street, and everyone who saw me thought I was mean. Little did they know that finding a family was my ultimate dream.

One day I was walking towards my favorite tree, when a big scary man came up and caught me.

He snatched me up in a big round net, even though I tried telling him I wasn't a threat.

He placed me in a crate in the back of his truck. I had run out of time; I had run out of luck.

When I opened my eyes, I was at someplace new. I did not know how to feel about it, so my thoughts began to brew.

I was in a big kennel. It was nice, but it wasn't cozy. All of the other dogs around me were being kind of nosey.

Life at Metro wasn't too grand.
Life in the crate was lonely, and
their food, bland.

The dogs next to me all found their new homes! I was happy for them, but I still felt all alone.

One day, to my surprise. A lady named Linlee happened to drop by. I was so happy I could have cried!

She took me outside and we played for hours! I worked up a sweat; and I needed a shower!

inlee stayed as long as
e could, and went back
home and told her
husband that her day
was good.

Linlee came back the next day to check on me! But on my kennel, there was a note that I could not see! It read not for adoption; How could this be?

I was sick, and there seemed to be no hope. Until I found out that Linlee had returned. Was this for real? Or was this a joke?

She took me outside, and I hopped in a truck. She looked at me and said, Penny, you're in luck.

I am now your Mom, and this man is your Dad. We are going to take care of you. There is no need to be sad.

A few months later, I was sick no more! I could jump on the bed and roll around on the floor.

My life was perfect, and my life was grand. But what was my purpose? I did not understand.

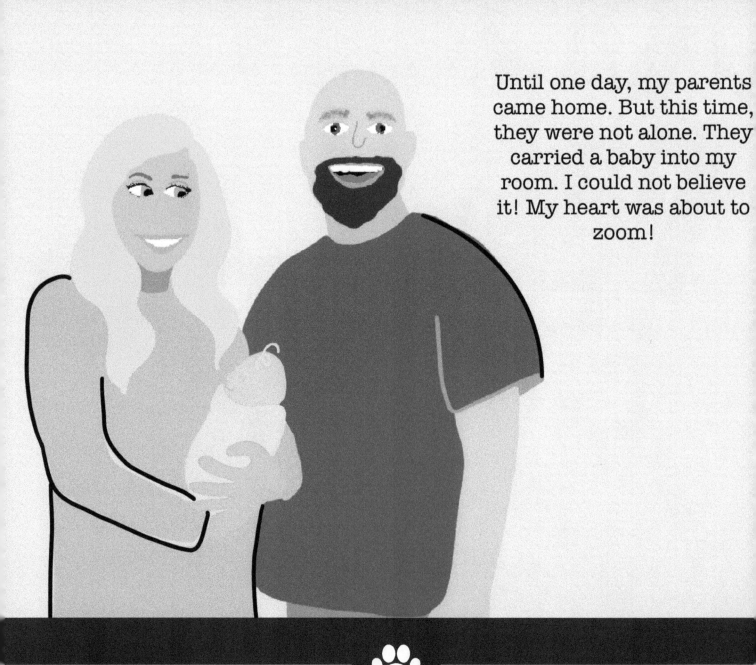

Until one day, my parents came home. But this time, they were not alone. They carried a baby into my room. I could not believe it! My heart was about to zoom!

My parents had brought me,
my own baby brother! Dad was
his father, and Mom was his
mother.

His name was Beckett, and to my surprise, he loves me with joy and a twinkle in his eye.

So, what is my purpose? It's simple, you see. To protect this brother that God has given me.

CPSIA information can be obtained
at www.ICGtesting.com
Printed in the USA
LVHW070428220221
679597LV00010B/49

9 780578 842059